YoungWriters POET

my favourite things

- A Time To Smile
Edited by Angela Fairbrace

 Young**Writers**

First published in Great Britain in 2007 by:
Young Writers
Remus House
Coltsfoot Drive
Peterborough
PE2 9JX
Telephone: 01733 890066
Website: www.youngwriters.co.uk

SB ISBN 978-1 84602 899 1

Foreword

'My Favourite Things' poetry competition indeed captured the imaginations of young writers across the nation as we received thousands of poems about what made the authors smile, laugh, feel happy and joyful whether it be a hobby, a pastime, an event, a person or something else.

We are proud to present *My Favourite Things - A Time To Smile.* So much thought, effort and creativity has been put into each and every poem cradled between these pages and we have enjoyed reading every single one. The task of selecting the overall winner was extremely enjoyable, but nevertheless a difficult task. You'll find the winner and runners-up at the front of this collection.

Young Writers was established in 1991 to promote poetry and creative writing to school children and encourage them to read, write and enjoy it. Here at Young Writers we are sure you'll agree that this fantastic edition achieves our aim and celebrates today's wealth of young writing talent. We hope you and your family continue to enjoy *My Favourite Things - A Time To Smile* for many years to come and hopefully inspire others to put pen to paper.

Contents

The Poems

My Favourite Things

I like nature, I like plants,
From the enormous elephants to the tiny ants.
The zoo is great, so's the sea,
I especially love to be me.

I like holidays, I like Mum and Dad,
Even though they are sometimes mad.
I love to ride my bike in the sun,
It is always really fun.

I like films, I like watching telly,
Eating sweets that fill my belly,
Pets and friends,
The fun never ends.

I like acting, I like to scream,
I always love custard on my ice cream.
Going home to my lovely house,
I'm glad our pet is a hamster, not a mouse.

I like presents, I like toys,
But I'm not so keen on all those boys.
I like my birthday, and Christmas too,
Little fat pigs and cows that moo.

Sophie Collett (7)

My Favourite Things

M any piles of assorted sweets waiting to be eaten
Y ellow sun sparkling every summer's day

F ountains of chocolate fondue surrounded by marshmallows
A nalysing anagrams in torn up puzzle books
V astly coloured flowers decorating my back garden
O livia and Sarah, my two best friends in the whole wide world
U naccountable mysteries hidden deep down in detective stories
R emarkable fireworks somersaulting in the night starry sky
I ncredible fresh snowflake carpets covering your driveway
T elevision blaring out your favourite movie
E erie, dark caves where owls or bears may live.

T ear-like icicles hanging from a frosted roof
H allowe'en, a chance to dress up and scare your mates
I rresistible puppies, just wanting to be loved
N o homework on school holidays
G oing to countries I have never been to before
S itting on my sofa, relaxing or playing video games.

Soshana Fernando (11)

A Few Of My Favourite Things

Shopping in the city,
Flashing the cash,
Having mates round,
Throwing a birthday bash.

Laughing with friends,
Sharing the fun,
Going on the cruise,
And laying in the sun.

Christmas and birthday,
Unwrapping the gifts,
Parking at the top of the car park,
And zooming down the lifts.

Listening to music,
Dancing and singing along,
On a Sunday morning,
When church bells go ding-dong.

These are a few of my favourite things.

Emma Mason (12)

My Favourite Things

What's quite cool,
Is going to school.

Maths is great,
But history I hate.

Running around,
In the playground.

The music I play,
After school every day.

Listening to bands,
That use their hands.

Bouncing and dancing,
Turning and prancing.

Getting treats,
While munching on sweets.

Watching TV,
Being called Niamhy.

And going places where there's fun,
Like Chessington.

Niamh Ayling (9)

My Favourite Things

These are my favourite things.
PlayStation and Game Boy.
These are my favourite things.
Pizza, pasta and chicken.
These are my favourite things.
Lollipops and chocolate chip cookies.
These are my favourite things.
Melons, strawberries and oranges.
These are my favourite things.
Beyblades and lightsabers.
These are my favourite things.
Harry Potter, Star Wars and Lilo and Stitch.
These are my favourite things.
Football, swimming and athletics.
These are my favourite things.
Roald Dahl books and Horrid Henry.
These are my favourite things.

Khem Liburd-Appiah

My Likes, Loves And Favourites

I like drawing, I love sleeping,
But my favourite is surfing on the highest waves.
I like swimming, I love talking.
But my favourite is riding bikes at the green grassy park,
I like shopping, I love eating,
But my favourite is playing instruments in the big musical world.
I like dancing, I love running,
But my favourite is jumping on a big bouncy trampoline.
I like singing, I love listening,
But my favourite is writing stories in my huge imaginative mind.
I like telling jokes, I love being tickled,
But my favourite is stroking animals with their soft silky fur.
I like playing tennis, I love making friends,
But my favourite is going to the cinema and eating popcorn!
I like reading, I love skating,
But my favourite is collecting items for charity for bargains!
I like designing, I love making,
But my favourite is opening presents because you never know what's
lurking inside.

Everyone has likes, everyone has loves,
But the favourites are what makes a person complete.

Rosalind Sheppard (10)

The Best Things In The World

Nintendo games, chocolate and sweets,
Playing outside in the hot sunny streets,
Listening to McFly and Pink sing,
Acting as a princess with a big sparkly ring,
At Hallowe'en when you get loads of sweets,
You go trick or treating on lots of streets,
Watching Top of the Pops where people are singing,
Calling for friends, keeping the doorbells ringing,
Going on holiday in the warm dazzling sun,
Diving in the swimming pool, having so much fun,
When the tooth fairy comes and leaves you money,
You get all excited and tell your mummy.
A kiss from your mum and a cuddle from your dad,
All these things make you so glad,
And at Christmas when Santa passes,
You get more accessories like sparkly glasses,
And at Easter when there's chocolate from the bunny,
There's none left cos it's all in Dad's tummy,
Out in the dark watching stars,
You fall asleep dreaming of Mars,
At birthday parties when you play games,
You meet new people and ask their names,
On the computer searching the net,
Sharing an umbrella when it's wet,
Always changing your room around,
Watching leaves swift on the ground,
Watching TV and stroking your pet,
Catching fish in a long green net,
Snuggling up tight ready for bed,
That's when your parents tuck you in and kiss your head.

Danni McCormack (10)

My Favourite Things

Outside with my friends,
All the fun never ends,
J K Rowling, Lemony Snicket,
In the sunshine playing cricket.

My mum and dad give me sweets,
Coke and Sprite and other treats.
Pizza and pasta with garlic bread,
Having a full tummy when I go to bed.

Reading books, watching TV,
Going on holiday by the sea.
Hamsters and kittens, rabbits and fish,
Roast chicken is my favourite dish.

Shouting and screaming,
Acting and dreaming.
Music, dancing, running around,
Playing my guitar to make a good sound.

Flowers and fresh rain,
Again and again.
When riding my bike I feel so free,
But most of all I love to be me!

Ellie Collett (9)

My Favourite Things

Hockey, netball, cricket, swimming,
Rugby, baseball, get the bat swinging,
I love exercise, I love sports,
I love games on different courts.

Chocolate, prawns, salmon, meat
Mussels and our cottage pie to eat
Everybody loves some food
There's a different one for every mood.

Easter, Christmas, Hallowe'en,
Ghosts and witches to make you scream,
Occasions are great, occasions are fun,
But my birthday is the best one.

Tracy Beaker one, two and three,
Double act, just for me,
Books are fab, authors are fun,
Jacqueline Wilson is the best one.

Hamster, gerbils, cats and dogs,
Rabbits and horses, but I don't like frogs,
Animals are cute, animals are sweet,
And they're more than just a lovely treat.

What you see here are my favourite things,
I also like to make my own necklaces and rings,
But there's a lot more things I'd like to do, like fly,
But I don't think I can so goodbye.

Lucy Bradshaw (10)

My Favourite Things

My favourite things
And the joy that brings,
The happiness and delight
Even the scary things that always give me a fright.
I like football, netball and having fun
When the whistle has been blown, the game has begun.
I like Man U, England and Doncaster Rovers
I like the luck I get from four-leaf clovers.
I like to cuddle a teddy bear,
They are soft, warm and it's like they care.
They will always be my favourite things
And the happiness that they bring,
But when they come to the end
The bestest thing is my best friend!

Sarah Newbitt (11)

Untitled

Football is the best, I don't know what's going to happen next.
I look at books every day, they make me feel I am drifting away.
I like a burger big and round,
Bonus in McDonalds they're only one pound.
I like the deadly tigers in the zoo, I can't believe they want to eat you.
Bananas are shaped like the moon,
Yellow like the sun too.
I like to stay up and play,
Mum says not late
OK!

Zack Mayer (9)

A-Z Of My Favourite Things

Ariel my awesome cat,
Being on holiday and having a chat.
Calling my friends and playing the flute,
Drinking pop in a new pair of boots.
Eclairs and candyfloss, eaten at the fair,
Fun days out, the wind blowing in my hair.
Ghost stories and midnight treats,
Huge gardens, like jungles with swinging seats.
I love my bedroom, lilac and pink,
Jumping on my trampoline, heart-shaped ice cubes in my drink.
KitKats and crisps with a crunch,
Listening to music and eating Sunday lunch.
Making snowmen and going swimming,
Nectarines, mangoes, running races and winning.
Origami fortune tellers and karaoke,
Parties and doing the hokey-cokey.
Queuing in Meadowhall to buy some shoes,
Ripping off wrapping paper at Christmas dos.
Sleepovers, sometimes gossiping all night,
Teacakes at B&Q, chips on Fright night.
Ursula Andress impressions from my brother,
Very funny! Show me another!
Wands and wizards in Harry Potter,
eXciting stories in my morning jotter.
Yippee my poem's nearly done,
Zany words and full of fun!

Holly Sandford (10)

Lola's Favourite Things

Flying in an aeroplane is really fun
Seeing butterflies fly in the sun
A smile comes to my face when McFly sing
Or when my best friend decides to ring.
Going to the shop 'Build-a-Bear'
Or spending time at a playful funfair
Singing along to some great CDs
Or watching my favourite show on TV
Kissing, cuddling, stroking my dog
Or watching tadpoles grow into frogs
Going to my swimming and gymnastics club
Or having lunch at a country pub.
Playing in the garden on the trampoline and swings
Or searching for the chocolate that the Easter Bunny brings . . .

Those are what I like to call my favourite things!

Lola Scriven (8)

My Favourite Things

Roses and violets, rosemary, thyme,
I'm number one, you are number nine,
Kittens and puppies, gerbils and fish;
Ice cream and popcorn; my favourite dish.
Cello and trumpet, violin, flute
My favourite transport's a train *'Toot toot'*
Cricket and tennis, rugby and ball,
Can't reach the net 'cause I'm not very tall.
Orange, purple, green and lime,
Roses and violets, rosemary, thyme.
My favourite things here for you
They will be there whatever you do.

Alys Murphy (10)

My Favourite Things

We love chocolate
We love sweets
We love Easter and Christmas treats!

We love pasta
We love pie
We love flying in the sky.

We love hockey
We love cricket
We read books by Lemony Snicket.

We love to cook
We love to bake
Especially when we bake pancakes!

Emily Dukes & Amy Best (10)

Some Of My Favourite Things

Playing singstar with my friends
Listening to them sing,
Along with board games and hide-and-seek,
Are my favourite things.

Walking my dog in the field,
Teaching him new tricks each day,
Throwing a ball and watching him play.

Having my friends over for a party,
We stay up late for a feast,
We dance and play and pillow fight,
Going to sleep is on our minds the least.

The horse I ride is called Rochelle,
I ride her in the ring,
I like to brush her mane and tail,
Even poo picking! I love everything!

Amelia Simpson (8)

These Are A Few Of My Favourite Things

These are a few of my favourite things
Listening when my favourite band sings
Playin' with my friend Emilia and going round her house
And listening to Jamillia
When I go right back home
I sometimes hog the phone
And when my sister gets into the bath
I always try to make her laugh
When I get into bed I always think I'm a sleepyhead.

Alishia Mason (8)

My Favourite Things

My favourite things
My favourite things are science club!
Blasting rockets out of little tubs
Pulleys and levers, magnets and forces
Causing trouble with circuits and torches!

My favourite things are golf in the sun
I long to score a hole in one
I love hitting my wood as far as I can,
And trying to keep my ball out of the sand!

My favourite things are building camps,
Blankets, cushions, pegs, books and lamps,
I take over the entire living room
Creating my very own 'Castle of doom!'

My favourite thing's riding my bike by the sea
Seeing how high I can climb in the tree,
Bouncing on my trampoline I love to play,
On my PlayStation I could spend all day.

My favourite things are drama on Friday
With all my friends I love to play
Games like Survival and Haunted House.

I pretend I am a pirate, a monster, a mouse!

Joshua Simpson (8)

A Few Of My Favourite Things

TV, Xbox, Gamecube fun, football, rugby, kung fu games,
Beckham, Bruce Lee, famous names.

Yu-gi-oh, Sponge-Bob . . . *Pop!* Can be fun too,
With characters playing funny games.

Charlie and me watching scary DVDs and me and Charlie
Playing on our bikes.

These are a few of my favourite things.

Jake Brennr Hirvela (8)

I Like These Things

Tearing around the field on my bike
Hiding and spying with my cousin
I watch dinosaurs on Prehistoric Park
Noisy Land Rovers driving by.
Good fun seeking out insects in the haystack
Swimming and diving in the pool.

I like these things.

Lazy cats wiggling their tails
I like crocodiles snapping in the sun.
Kites flying high in the sky
Eating sweets and ice cream.

Bradley Cain (8)

Favourite Things

I have always loved chocolate and sweets,
In fact I enjoy a whole pile of treats
If I'm good I get lots and I'm glad
But if I'm bad I get none and I'm sad.

Michael Carty (8)

Some Things I Like

I go out in the hot red sun
I play with my football, it is great fun.

I like to watch wrestling
It's all on TV
I usually find it on Sky Sports 3.

I like Mr Sweatman
I like his hair
I like his tie and his swivelly chair.

This is a poem
By Charlie Banks, I hope you like
With many thanks.

Charlie Banks (8)

My Favourite Things

Ferraris and Porsches with shiny new features
Tigers and lions and all of God's creatures
Rugby and football, judo and swims
These are a few of my favourite things.

'When I'm tired
When I'm annoyed
When I'm feeling mad
I simply remember my favourite things
And then I don't feel so bad.'

Surfing on the Internet and games on the PS2
Vegetables, meat and fresh fruit are great too!
Speaking to friends, when the phone rings,
These are a few of my favourite things.

'When I'm tired
When I'm annoyed
When I'm feeling mad
I simply remember my favourite things
And then I don't feel so bad.'

Riding my bike, running home
Playing in the bath, getting covered in foam
Listening to my dad, when he sings
These are a few of my favourite things.

Christopher Richards (9)

My Favourite Things

A hug from my mummy,
And warm soup in my tummy.
Playing with Dizzy,
And drinking drinks that are fizzy.
Playing my recorder,
And cycling fast round a corner.
Doing abstract art,
And taking part in drama lessons with friends.

Swimming at my local pool,
And having a game of netball.
Easing lots of yummy cheese,
And running around in a cool breeze.
Bouncing on the trampoline,
Birthdays, Christmas, Hallowe'en.

Emily Gawler (8)

These Are A Few Of My Favourite Things!

Sparkling jewellery in the shop window
Teddies snuggled in my bed
Clouds passing by as I look at the sky
Cuddles while the telly is on
Adventures through the woods at night
Music and sleepovers make me feel great
The sound of the wind on a new Christmas morning
Irn-Bru and chocolate straight from the fridge
Shopping for my bits 'n' bobs, like rings and belts, shoes and bags,
Finally sitting down and looking through my mum's treasure box
At the old . . . and the new.
These are a few of my favourite things!

Rachael White (12)

My Favourite Thing!

My favourite thing!
Being an actor
Teachers and scientists
Even a doctor.

My favourite thing!
Learning and playing
I go to the beach
Resting and playing.

My favourite thing!
My sister Raisa
She's so cute
And nothing is nicer.

My favourite thing!
Reading and writing
Being creative,
Stitching and sewing.

My favourite thing!
Playing with a toy
Whenever I play with one
It's always a joy.

My favourite thing!
Thoughts are flowing
I try so hard
Writing a poem!

Mahfara Ahmed (8)

My Favourite Things

Playing in the sun,
Having fun,
Visiting friends,
Hallowe'en and Christmas,
These are some of my favourite things.

Reading a good book,
Drawing with pens,
Playing with the dog,
And eating food,
These are some of my favourite things.

Watching TV
The occasional sweet,
Staying in, by the fire,
Being really cheeky,
These are some of my favourite things.

Not tidying my room,
A hug from my sister,
Birthdays and parties,
Sleeping in late!
These are all of my favourite things.

Bethany Swallow (8)

My Favourite Things

Playing football
Scoring goals
Playing on my PS2
Are some of the favourite things I like to do.

Hanging around with my friends
Telling funny jokes that make me laugh
Having lots of nice hot baths
Are some of the favourite things I like to do.

Watching my favourite show The Simpsons
Stroking furry sheep
And getting a good night's sleep
Are some of the favourite things I like to do.

Abu-Bakar Miah (11)

My Favourite Things

Like all the children on the planet Earth,
I love my thoughtful mum, who raised me since my birth,
I like my toys, PlayStation 2
And I enjoy to watch a movie titled 'Doctor Who'.

To all, I like to play on my computer,
And I am happy to study with my drama school tutor,
I like my friends, who faithfully stand up for me,
I pray to God, that let it all to be.

But!

My favourite things,
Would be bright rising sun,
And my favourite things,
Would be blue and clear sky.

Would be white fluffy clouds,
And green juicy grass,
Mixed with colourful flowers,
Mixed with bees and with harmony pass.

All this favourite things,
Make me happy and play,
All these favourite things,
It is sign for *peace*.

Maksym Zhylin (9)

A Few Of My Favourite Things

Meeting new people and having a laugh,
Playing outside on the fresh green grass,
Acting and dancing, gymnastics too,
These are a few of my favourite things.

From dogs and horses, monkeys and cats,
The feel of satin cushions and woolly hats,
Melting chocolate and chunks of sweet pineapple,
These are a few of my favourite things.

The sound of my siblings, fighting over sweets,
Girls Aloud's album, listening to the rhythmic beats,
Trampolines, bikes, I love sporty things!
These are a few of my favourite things.

Snuggling up on the sofa and watching TV,
Warm baths with bubbles all smothered around me,
Writing stories, poems and creative drawings,
These are a few of my favourite things.

Apples, grapes and exotic fruits,
From PE trainers to designer boots,
The high-tech objects like iPods and phones,
These are a few of my favourite things.

From my brother and sister to Granny and Gramps,
Using my bike to go over high ramps,
Family is the most important thing,
This is probably my favourite thing!

Kayley Midlane (11)

My Favourite Things

I like chocolate, Christmas presents too
Learning English and playing with Chou Chou.
Then there's my cheerleading, that's a favourite thing
Playing my music and having a sing.
Splashing and diving, getting wet in the pool
Swimming lessons are so cool.
Watching DVDs with my brother in bed and
Snuggling up with Millie Ted.
They are all my favourites, what can I say
I like them all in their own little way.

Hannah Price (8)

My Favourite Things (or What Makes Me Happy)

Happiness is wearing any clothes which are pink.

Happiness is playing with my favourite toys.

Happiness is waking up early on Christmas morning to a huge pile
of presents.

Happiness is reading a very interesting story.

Happiness is a large bowl of delicious, chocolate ice cream.

Happiness is going to swimming and gymnastics lessons.

Happiness is being lucky enough to have a warm, comfortable home.

Happiness is holidays in sunny Italy.

Happiness is having a kind and considerate older brother.

Happiness is lots of friends who care about me.

Happiness is enough food never to feel really hungry.

Happiness is a lovely teacher at school, who helps me to learn.

Happiness is having a fit and healthy body.

Happiness is having an active and inquisitive mind.

Happiness is my mummy and daddy, who love me dearly.

Happiness is the precious gift of being one of God's special children.

Ciaran Jasper (11)

My Favourite Things

Dolls and roller skates,
Fancy dressing with my mates,
Teddy bears and skipping ropes,
Reading books with lots of jokes.

Dancing and singing,
Acting and bowling,
Going on holidays,
Partying in so many ways.

Lollipops and fudge cake,
Ice cream with chocolate flake,
Hallowe'en, Christmas, Easter too,
Means lots of treats for me and you.

I love watching television,
When psychic Raven has a vision,
High School Musical, the Cheetah Girls 2,
I like to watch these, I think you would too.

Maths, English and geography,
PE, art and history,
Those are the subjects I like the best,
Except when it's time to take a test.

My favourite time most of all,
Is family time, we have a ball,
We play games and watch telly,
And of course we fill our belly.

Amy Staniford (10)

All My Favourite Things!

My favourite things I have quite a few,
So listen up, I'll tell them to you
I like to play most of the sports,
They're fun and active and there's all sorts.
I also like to be quite lazy too,
Flick through the TV channels, one, four, three, two.
And I like to hang around with my friends as well,
To visit the shops and see what they sell.
In the sun I enjoy a nice long holiday,
Even if it can be quite a bit to pay.
And spaghetti is what I like to eat,
Sitting at the dinner table on my seat.
And music I like to listen to,
But normally when there's nothing to do.
I also like to do art, whether it's just drawing,
As long as it's something not very boring.
On the computer I like to doodle around,
Maybe changing the settings or the sound.
Another of my favourite things is,
Ice in a glass of Coca-Cola fizz
But my most favourite thing has to be,
Hanging about at home, just being me!

Shaylea Merrick (12)

My Favourite Thing Is My Pets

My pets are really cute
They try to catch rats
Oh they are so cute
I always salute
At them
And when
I stroke them they purr
Madam and sir
Moonlight and Minstrel oh so cute
They purr so much that they're never on mute
I think the world of my cute cats
Even if they catch a rat!

Kathleen Ryan (8)

My Favourite Things

My favourite things in the world are
Lego, I enjoy putting it together
I also love doing history on the PC for my teacher and me
When I come home from school
I play on the computer, although I might
Go to my room and play on my PlayStation 2
And say 'Come on, bring it on.'
I would play football on Saturday at 10am
And then go to the park to build a den.
When I go camping I do wheelies on my cool red bike
Around the big open green campsite.
On a hot Sunday morning I might go swimming
But only if my dad's willing
Then go to Sportsworld and look for Chelsea stuff for my room.
Then go to McDonald's and have a Happy Meal or two.
In the afternoon I play a game of cards called Beanie
Then go save some penalties in a game of footie.
Now that is just some of my favourite things
If you want to know the rest then give me a ring!

Thomas Shepherd (9)

My Favourite Things

My most favourite things are my CDs
Then everything else comes next
My next favourite thing is my mobile phone
I love to phone and text
Then come my cuddly toys
My favourite toy is called Tom
Next comes my necklaces
I love the one that is black
Then comes my trousers
My favourite pair are my black combats
So that's all my favourite things rolled into one
Now my favourite poem is done.

Lauren Blaikie (10)

My Favourite Things

This life I love, the pleasure it brings
These are a few of my favourite things.

Sitting by the campfire flames
Toasting marshmallows, playing games
Watching the stars twinkle above
Sit with my family, know that I'm loved.

My family around me, I'm safe and secure
We're happy together, who could want more?
My mum, dad, sister and me
We mustn't forget our rescue dog, Phoebe!

Phoebe the dog joins in the fun
A walk in the field, she longs to run
My never judging man's best friend
Enjoys the beach and a swim at the end.

Down on the beach, riding the waves
Exploring the rock pools, sea life and caves
When the sun makes me tired, I welcome a break
With a huge fat ice cream and a big scrumptious flake.

Ben and Jerry - the kings of ice cream
Phish Food and Cookie Dough, taste like a dream
Chocolate Fudge Brownie scooped high in a bowl
A mountain of ice cream is good for the soul!

This life I love, the pleasure it brings
Those were a few of my favourite things.

Jess Smith (11)

My Favourite Things

I love to go swimming
And I'm always winning.
Then I play basketball,
In the school hall.
Then I play football,
With a big fat ball.
When it's time to go home,
I feel all alone,
But then I think,
My dad's at home.
When I get home my dad takes me to play,
Oh I had such a good day.

Zainab Shuja (9)

My Favourite Things

I like the sound of the birds singing early in the morning
That's my favourite time of the morning.
I like the smell of my toast every morning
I like it when my teacher tells me to do some drawing,
But most of all I like it when my daddy hugs me when I am yawning.

Hareena Kaur (8)

My Favourite Things

These favourite things I've written down for you,
Are just a selected few.
So, go on, take a seat.
Make a cup of tea,
And move near the heat.

Most of my favourite things are sports,
Especially badminton on the indoor courts.
Quiet like pool or loud like football,
Apart from rugby, I love them all.

I can't wait until Scribble comes,
Writing poetry with silly puns.
I really like the stories, they're ace,
But the puzzles are the best, that's the case.

Camping I really love,
Especially eating the food.
Snowballs coming from high above,
And sledging in the nude.

A hobby of mine has to be,
Going to the cinema and watching TV
What else I like is the PS2
And on my favourite game, the car flew.

Cookery is a passion,
The brandy snap I make will get your teeth gnashing
My speciality is curry,
And believe me, it will make you go to the loo in a hurry.

My favourite list could go on and on,
Until I have no paper to write upon.
So, now I'll have to fly,
For my friends await me,
Therefore I shall say goodbye.

Luke Woodhead (12)

My Favourite Things Poem

Jumping on the sofa and hanging out with friends,
Shopping till I drop and picking all the latest trends,
Listening to Beyonce and Justin Timberlake,
Getting into trouble; that's the route I take.

Stuffing my face with chocolate and playing on my PS2,
Wearing all my make-up, blush, mascara, lipgloss too,
Singing to my heart's content and fab piano playing,
Jacqueline Wilson's brilliant books and on the beach, sunbathing.

Grandma's special kisses and Mummy's special cuddles,
I do enjoy in autumn, splashing in big wet puddles.
Playing Bratz and stroking cats - watching TV and
On Hallowe'en I trick or treat with sweeties in my hand!

I also wear some golden jewels and silver necklaces,
Performing on a big wide stage, I really love showbiz!
I also wear some multicoloured thumb-sized different rings,
I wonder if some of these are *your* favourite things?

Katie Gardner-Edwards (10)

My Friend Miles

I ride a horse called Miles
He meets me with his smiles
I put on his saddle and on the beach we paddle
Miles loves to swim and I love to ride him.

Aaron Whalin (11)

My Favourite Things

I have lots of different things,
And I will tell you them all;
First there's football, the best sport,
Then there's chocolate for the food
Going around your friend's house,
And playing Xbox and Nintendo DS,
When bored kicking things around the house,
When happy, go down the park.
At school the best is PE and ICT,
At the shops or in town looking at
Football things or toys.
My favourite family member
Is my dog Bosun, he's so cute.
My favourite toys are cars.
I have lots of favourite things,
I love having parties, holidays,
And more,
I love hugging and kissing
My mum and dad,
Who are sometimes mad.
I love going to concerts, reading a book,
Drawing on paper,
Watching my big brother cook.
And making up shows,
Dressing up weird,
Watching football
And when my friends and little brother are around,
Wearing a fake beard.

Daniel Wells (10)

My Favourite Things

Singing, dancing, drama and cycling,
They're some of my favourite things.

Chess, snooker and other games,
They're so fun to play.

Rugby, football, darts and tennis,
They're definitely great sports.

Friends and family also love,
They're there when I need them.

Collecting red elastic bands for my elastic band ball!
They're always lying on the pavement, I collect them one and all.

I have lots and lots of favourite things, too many really to mention,
But my most favourite thing of all is being with my family watching
television.

Jacob Stephens (9)

Hallowe'en

Hallowe'en, Hallowe'en
Why is it soooo much fun?
You can have Hallowe'en cakes in a bun!

Scary faces, devil's delights, witches flying in the night,
Trick or treaters come to meet us
Hoping for money, sweets and treats
Which we spend and eat in a week.

Black cats, spiders and bats
Skeletons, pumpkins and witches' hats
Running through the streets like bats.

Hallowe'en, Hallowe'en is my favourite time
Dunking for apples, dressing up and making treats
I wouldn't change it for a dime!

Kate Pearce (8)

My Favourite Things

A magician, he stands on the stage tonight
And waves his long pointy wand
Over the rim of his tall purple hat
And out spill a parade of my favourite things.

Dogs with black patches over their eyes
Race over the star-patterned brim
An intricate snowflake from a cold winter's day
Slowly creeps out of the topper.

Up on the edge a pair of ice skating boots glide
Unwilling to leave the indigo ring of silk

Next blossom forth a garden of books
Stepping out boldly in order of favourite to least
Presents all done up in exotic paper gamble forwards in turn
A thousand ribbons meet at their head, loops of golden glitter bows.

Letters fall as they do when you receive mail
Crisp and white, stiff and loaded with excitement
Christmas baubles full of irresistible sparkling charm
Grace sweeping bows of majestic pines.

Then oh wonder of wonders, my most favourite thing
Standing there on the brim
Flapping like a gaggle of geese
The ones I laugh with
The ones I joke with
The ones who make a dark day seem light.

They're my wonderful friends

The show is over, the magician has gone
But my favourite things remain, grouped around me
Igniting the light in my heart.

Laura Smith (11)

My Favourite Things

Playing with my dog, slobbery licks all the time!
Waiting for my birthday when I may turn nine.
Reading a good book and smiling when Green Day sing
These are a few of my favourite things.

Riding my pony and cycling my bike,
Playing with my teddy who I named Mike.
Camping abroad, catching butterflies with nice wings,
These are only some of my favourite things.

Playing outside when the weather is good
Eating lots of very yummy food.
Laughing and putting my hands over my ears when the church bell
rings,

These are more of my favourite things.

Watching TV and kissing my mum
Hugging my dad and having lots of fun
Writing stories and going on the swings
These are most of my favourite things.

Flora Chirnside (9)

My Family

My favourite things are my family,
My mum and my bruv,
They are such wonderful people,
I think I'm in love.

My brother is Dan,
He annoys me when he can,
We argue and fight,
But he's really alright.

My mum is called Sue,
She cheers me when I'm blue,
She is lovely when she smiles,
To see it I would walk miles.

We all live together,
I hope forever,
The last thing I have to say,
To Daniel and Sue,
Is I love you and I always will do!

Amy Harrison (10)

Just A Few Of My Favourite Things

We got my phone that's special to me,
And all of my books that I love to read,
On a quiet day when there's nothing to do,
I'll curl up on the sofa,
With a book by Jimmy O'loo,
These are just a few of my favourite things.
When I'm a bit sad and feeling low,
My dog will come and cheer me up,
By sitting on my lap all warm and friendly,
Or even when I'm bored at home,
I'll take out my hamster and watch him play in his cage,
Running round and round in his little wheel,
These are just a few of my favourite things.
Or just spending time with all my mates,
Is just enough to keep me entertained,
I have so many friends,
They are all so loyal and comforting to me,
I love my family, they are absolutely crazy,
But when you need the most,
You can guarantee they will be around,
These are just a few of my favourite things.
I play on my PlayStation 'til Mum gets me off
And giggle with my pals,
As we share secrets at sleepovers
Or just sitting at school with a teacher nagging
Is just enough for me!
So now I've told you
Just a few of my favourite things!

Hannah Murray (11)

My Favourite Things

M y favourite things
Y ou, my mum and dad,

F amily, friends
A unties, uncles
V ampires, ghosts
O ranges, apples
U nusual orang-utans, chimps
R ivers flowing
I ce melting
T ree at Christmas time
E lves helping Santa

T insel twinkling
H appy faces
I nnocent children
N ew Year parties
G rass growing
S un shining

These are my favourite things.

Cory Wild (11)

A Day Full Of My Favourite Things

I'd start with Shreddies
To fill me up,
Then a quick game of snakes and ladders
Before school,
I'd sit next to my best friend Ellie
And give her a hug,
Have crisps with my lunch
Then play 'stuck in the mud'
I'd bend and roll at gymnastics club
To get me fit,
Then definitely have sausages for tea
With tomato sauce.
I'd read 'The Jolly Little Postman'
At bedtimo,
Kiss all my family goodnight
Cuddle Charlie my toy dog,
And sleep.

Robert Whorton (6)

My Mum And Dad

My mum shines like a star
My mum drives a nice blue car
She is witty and wonderful and has a degree
I love her just like she loves me.

My dad likes to watch football
The chances of him missing a match are very, very small
My dad snores as loud as can be
I love him, just like he loves me!

I love my mum and dad
If I didn't have them, things would be bad
Sometimes I feel like selling them for no fee
But I still love them like they love me!

Nichole Maddison (11)

My Favourite Hobbies

My favourite hobby is drawing nice things
I long to be an artist
Drawing is my hobby.

My favourite hobby
Is reading a book
Because my mind goes wild
Reading is my hobby.

My favourite hobby
Is acting out a play
I'd love to be an actress
Acting is my hobby.

These are my hobbies
Do you have a hobby?
Because I'd love to
Hear from you.

Katie Whitehouse (9)

The Things I Love The Most!

Running in the garden, playing on the swing
I love doing this, it's my favourite thing.
Sweet is my horse Wensley, he is my bestest friend
I love him very dearly and our friendship will never end.
All the little birdies singing in the trees,
Butterflies and ladybirds and even bumblebees.
Making friendship bracelets with some pretty beads
Plant some big sunflowers with sunflower seeds.
Ice creams and sweets are a real treat
These are some things that I love to eat.
Ballet and Brownies and even football
And then going swimming in the swimming pool.
Doing lots of CDs, playing lots of tapes
Then going downstairs to get some yummy grapes.
Cassandra, Cybermen and Daleks too
I love all these characters from Doctor Who.
I guess you now know some of my favourite things
Like running in the garden and playing on the swing,
These are some things that I love to do
So why don't you go and try them too.

Millie Hicks (9)

My Enjoyment

I love the sea's swirling sound
The waves pattering on the shore,
The sound of people splashing,
Shouting, having fun.

Seeing friends makes me smile,
Laughing
Playing
Talking
Just being in their company
Is a joy to me.

Going out with my family
Is always a laugh
Chooky Dad from Scotland
Jolly Mum from Leeds
Funny Ben, from Brayton
And me; a good all-rounder,

That's a few of my favourite things.

Byrony McFarlane (11)

Hobby

H ow I love to swim and play
   games at any time of day
O ther things are singing,
   singing in the garden whilst swinging on the swing
B y the end of the day
   piano and recorder is what I play.
B ye-bye, bye-bye is what I regret,
   When we go on holiday to say to my pet
Y ippee, yippee, I love to play
   On my computer, but not every day!

Laura Filipe (9)

These Are A Few Of My Favourite Things

I love shopping in spring
And to get lots of bling
I love hanging with my friends
These are a few of my favourite things.

I love Hallowe'en
I'd like to be a vampire queen
I love to have lunch with my mum
These are a few of my favourite things.

I love playing my guitar
I'd love to get a sports car
I love to watch TV
These are a few of my favourite things.

I love to eat sweets
And to have nice clean bed sheets
But best of all I love to swim
These are a few of my favourite things.

I love to ride my skateboard
When I do that I don't get bored
I love doing my hair
These are a few of my favourite things.

I love to bake cakes
And to go fishing in the lake
I really love Lilly Allen
These are a few of my favourite things.

Georgie Read (10)

My Favourite Things

I love dancing, singing and playing games
Going for a walk and getting ice cream
Trips to the beach and playing in the sand
Feeding my cows and standing on my land
These are a few of my favourite things
But most of all I wish I had wings.

Tara McParland (7)

My Favourite Things

I love playing football
It's my favourite thing
If I didn't have my football
I wouldn't have anything.

Besides the football
I like the golf too
And when my friends lose
They go boo-hoo!

I love playing Yu-Gi-Oh
Especially with my mates
We duel and swap cards
It's really, really great.

There's too many things to think of
I haven't even begun
Swimming, holidays and my bicycle
They're always lots of fun.

So now I've told you
Some of my favourite things
But do you know what I'd really like?
To fly like a bird with wings.

Callum O'Neill (8)

My Favourite Things

Dancing, prancing, singing and playing,
These are the things I do when I'm free -
Afternoon and evening.
At the weekend.
Swimming and splashing.
Down in the pool.
Hallowe'en and scary things
Ghosts and ghouls popping out
Playing with my friends
Climbing trees high and low
But most of all
I love best
Playing with my dog.

Laura Goodman (9)

My Favourite Things

Christmas time brings great cheer
It's one of my favourite times of year
I love sweets and special treats.
They are so nice and sticky.
I love Disneyland with Minnie and Mickey
I like snow and teddy bears.
They are so light and fluffy.
Dogs are lovely but sometimes can be scruffy.
I love birthday parties
I see all my friends
I always feel sad when they end.

Jena McDermott (8)

My Favourite Things

I love Mummy
I love Daddy.
I love my brother and my sister
Every night I pray to God
To keep them safe and happy.

Aaron Duffy

Poetry Is Fun For Everyone

Horse riding on my course,
I enjoy jumping and playing on my horse.
I love to play with my friends at parties,
After school again and again.
Birthdays and presents I like to receive,
Eating ice cream and sweets and pennies to spend.
Watching TV and going to school, learning about day to day rules.
These are a few of my favourite things!

Georgina Shilling (8)

My Favourite Things

I like watching DVDs
My favourite two are the Pink Panther and Scooby-Doo.
I like books, like The Hungry Otter,
But my favourite is Harry Potter.
These are some of my favourite things.

When my mum says it's bath time
I get happy because it's the best pastime,
I really love my cosy, warm bed,
I like to snuggle up with my ted!
These are some of my favourite things.

My family is better than the rest
Especially my brother Matt, he's the best.
I love all my mates, for example Tara
But my best friend's name is Lara.
These are some of my favourite things.

I like clothes very, very much
The best make by far is Von Dutch.
I like to make my hair look all that
I love it when it's in a plait.
These are some of my favourite things.

I really, really like animals a lot
Especially my pet dog called Spot,
I love toys like my space rocket
My dolls and my Polly Pocket.

These are *all* of my favourite things.

Rebecca Dawson (10)

Chocolate

Chocolate, I love chocolate
The smooth smell, sweet, delicate and lovely.
Smell the thick and tasty treat,
The big chocolate, just imagine the thick and lustre smell
And the melting blocks in your hands
Just running through your hands pouring down your body,
And all the gorgeous taste.
Chocolate is beautiful and smooth,
Just imagine taking a nice enormous bite then licking your lips
And tasting all the melted flavours.

Jordon Bahadur (10)

My Favourite Things!

Playing my guitar
And watching TV
Feeding and washing
My tortoise Sparky
These are a few of my favourite things.

At school chasing boys
At home playing Eye Toy
Don't forget to mention
My passion for fashion
These are a few of my favourite things.

With hobbies and activities
Each and every day of the week
One of my favourite things
At the weekend is to sleep!

Robyn Critcher (9)

My Family

M um and Dad are always there,
Y es! Helping us achieve

F un and lovely, also taking care.
A lways there when needed.
M otivating and cool,
I love my family, brothers and all,
L ively and fun,
Y es they're my family.

My family are really cool.

Zoe Brown (10)

Favourite Things

When butterflies are flying and when a colourful bird sings,
These are two of my favourite things,
When my bunny is jumping, jumping mad,
When it's night-time and the door opens 'Yeah, it's Dad!'
Diving and splashing in the blue salty sea,
And sitting on the edge, crab fishing, on Devon's Quay.
When it's time for Christmas and only one night to go,
On Bonfire Night when all is aglow,
Whilst a cake is baking it smells so good,
In wintertime splashing in all the mud,
When it's the last day of term and school is out,
All it makes me want to do is shout,
Listing my favourite things is really hard to do,
Because I have sooo many favourite things, it is true.

Rebecca Baldwin (10)

My Favourite Things

Stars - stars in the dark sky floating like diamonds
Butterflies - butterflies' golden wings sparkling in the sun
Ice cream - ice cream is yummy and I love it!
Fairies - fairies are pretty and tiny
Books - when I read them I get all excited
Flowers - sweet-smelling and colourful
Rainbows - lots of shining colours
Friends - you can trust them
Mums and Dads - mums and dads give you hugs and kisses
Brothers - brothers are so annoying
Dogs - my gorgeous dog - Tilly.

Emma Green (8)

My Favourite Things

My favourite things include diamonds and rings
Puppies and laptops and prezzies that Father Christmas brings,
Skirts, money, my mum and my friends,
Exciting emails that family always send!
My boyfriend is a special part of my life too.
I also love having to write poems, it gives me something to do.
I like the singers Shayne Ward and Britney Spears
And the song Shout Out by Tears For Fears.
I love to eat chocolate ice cream and ice poles
I really like cute baby foals!
I admire the Tower of London and I like the subway
I could also be swimming my socks off in a lovely cold pool all day!

Chloë Brown (9)

My Favourite Things

Cute, fluffy hamsters and fun playful puppies,
Fat loving cats that stay sleeping for hours,
White fluffy bunnies that jump round and round,
These are a few of my favourite things.

Dairy milk chocolate and creamy French Milko,
My mum's roast dinners and my dad's flapjacks,
Going to the beach and eating ice cream,
These are a few of my favourite things.

Writing fun stories and dreaming up poems,
Reading a good book and playing on my keyboard,
Listening to music for hours on end,
These are a few of my favourite things.

When the cat bites,
When the wasp stings,
When I'm feeling sad,
I simply remember my favourite things
And then I don't feel so bad!

Chloe Britton (10)

My Favourite Things

Here are some of my favourite things
See if you like them too.

Eating sticky mixture
When I'm baking cakes with Mummy
I like having water fights
When the weather's warm and sunny.

I like playing pool with Luke and Dad
Winner's the one to pot the black
Love biking in the park
Over the bumps and around the track.

At Grandma's I'm Robin Hood
Firing arrows from up in the tree
She turns up the fire, gets out the sweets
Makes hot chocolate and we watch TV.

I like going swimming when it's dark
There's not many in the pool
I can jump and splash as much as I want
I think it's really cool.

Sometimes when it's night-time
I read Asterix in bed
I get all snuggled up
Have a cuddle with my ted.

I hope you like my poem
Now it's time for me to go
I'm off to listen to a story tape
And make ships with my Lego.

Ben Woodhead (9)

Football

The roar of the crowd
It excites me so
The back of the net
Is where the ball shall go
First Fabregas, then Henry
Then Adebayor, that makes it three
I love maths and English too
But football is my first love
And it always will be too.

Samuel Davis (8)

I Like To . . .

I like to be creative,
I like to sing and dance.
I like to make my own clothes,
I like to take a chance.

With lots of people all around,
I like to talk things out.
I like to smile and not frown,
But sometimes scream and shout.

I like to ride my bike,
I like to watch TV,
Best of all,
I like to just be me.

Rebekah Royle (10)

My Favourite Things

I love riding my bike with its big round wheels
Wearing a sparkly crash helmet and shoes with high heels!
I like being silly, having a giggle and fun
Eating sweets with my friends and a massive iced bun
I like to go shopping for frilly girly clothes
And buy earrings and lipgloss and hair toggles and bows
And when I am tired I love a big cuddle
With my mum and my dog and in a big squeezy huddle
Diving into bed at the end of the day
When I'm sleepy but happy after a fun day of play
Dressed in Princess pyjamas and crown on my head
I float off to sleep and rise straight off the bed!
I soar in the air with my favourite teddy bear
Flying like a fairy with a tiara in my hair
Wearing bright-coloured wings on a magical flight
Dancing in the air and screaming with delight
Nose-diving to Earth with a wave of my wand
I bounce on a trampoline and avoid the fish pond!
Back up in the air I jump on a cloud
It's fluffy and pink and makes me laugh out loud
Along comes Minty a unicorn to ride
I leap on her back and she takes long flying strides
We go to a party with other magical friends
And I want the night to never ever end
I dress up for a party and eat jelly and jam
With my favourite friends and toys in Fairy Land
I awake in the morning with a big happy smile
And skateboard to school for it's only a mile
And everything I do makes me bounce and spring
Because all of these joys are my favourite things.

Eleanor Coveney (9)

My Favourite Things

Being with my friends and having fun,
Taking long holidays in the sun,
Going to the cinema watching a funny movie,
Me and my little sister making a chocolate smoothie.

The weekend has arrived, time to go shopping,
Going into every shop without even stopping.
Chilling in my bedroom, listening to the groove,
Grabbing my hairbrush and dancing with great moves.

Riding my bike I feel I'm in a race,
My sisters just can't keep up with my pace,
Me and my cousin going for a swim,
Splashing about both of us with a grin.

I like to watch a movie on TV
When it's just me and my family,
My mum and dad take us to the swings,
These are a few of my favourite things!

Georgina Dance (11)

Happiness

Playing in the sun
Having good fun
Riding my bike
When flying a kite
These are a few of my favourite things.

Playing on my PlayStation
Playing my favourite games
Swimming with my friends
Let's hope our relationship never ends
These are a few of my favourite things.

The smell of freshly cut grass
Autumn leaves blowing in the breeze
The smell of winter in the air
All wrapped up with that winter glow
With not very far to go
These are a few of my favourite things.

Bethany Wild (11)

My Favourite Things

I like watching cartoons and discovering things,
Going to the park and playing on the swings.
Eating chocolate, plenty of sweets,
And when Mummy and Daddy give me a treat

I like reading adventure books,
Especially the one about Captain Hook.
Christmas is my favourite time,
Presents and turkey and singing Christmas rhymes.

Visiting friends and having fun,
Splashing about in the pool in the sun.
Singing along with McFly,
These are a few of my favourite things.

Jonathan Wilson (8)

My Favourite Things

Having fun,
Playing in the sun.
Talking with friends,
Gossiping about the new trends.
They're my favourite things. What are yours?

Mum giving me treats,
Dad giving sweets.
A hug delivered to me,
A beautiful kiss that I can see.
They're my favourite things. What are yours?

Playing with my pet,
Scoring a goal in the back of the net.
Reading a poem book,
Not letting my sister have a look.
They're my favourite things. What are yours?

Making stuff out of glue,
Sticking stuff that is blue.
Trying to sew
A pink bow.
They're my favourite things. What are yours?

Running round a tree,
Splashing in the sea.
Playing with cats,
Visiting caves where there are bats.
They're my favourite things. What are yours?

Watching a baby eating cold ice cream,
Seeing their cute faces gleam.
Entering my poems in competitions,
Winning or losing doesn't matter to me.
They're my favourite things. What are yours?

Nazehat Uddin (12)

Are These A Few Of Your Favourite Things?

Xbox games and watching the TV,
Off on holiday by the wavy sea.
Going in the garden, playing on the swings,
Are these a few of your favourite things?

Drama and parties and having fun,
Having sweets and chocolate buns.
Going to school, learning about the Tudor kings,
Are these a few of your favourite things?

Christmas and music and being cheeky too,
Making stuff out of paper and glue.
Watching the famous Kylie sing,
Are these a few of your favourite things?

Sunbathing and swimming, writing as well,
Going to the beach and picking up shells.
Making bracelets and also rings,
Are these a few of your favourite things?

Listening to music and reading a good book,
Trying on the latest fashion with the new look.
Putting on all my bling,
Are these a few of your favourite things?

Tallulah Moody (9)

My Favourite Things

Shimmering in light,
Flying like a kite.
Shining here and there,
Woven with care.
I stop and grin,
Look at all the work put in.
A spider does take its time
And works with detail every line.
When the rain falls
Into little pools,
The beauty shimmers
And rain glimmers.
A spider's web in the rain,
It is not the just plain old same.

My family and friends,
A bond that never ends.
These mean all the world to you,
No matter what they say or do.
If you're ever feeling alone,
Don't forget just give them a phone.
Friends and family are valuable things,
Locking them in your safe with your rings.
If you're stuck or in stress,
Call them round and then confess.
Don't be afraid they will not bite,
But don't be afraid to say they're right.
If you're feeling low or feeling fine,
They'll always be there rain or shine.

Everyone has their favourite things,
Whether its PlayStations or diamond rings.

Katie Cudmore (11)

These Things Are Right For Me

Hanging with my friends,
I hate things when they end.
Going to the park, playing on the swings.
These are just a few of *my* favourite things.

Listening to my music tunes,
sitting there watching cartoons.
Love watching Most Haunted live,
like going swimming and trying to dive.

I love reading all my books,
especially the ones that get me really hooked.
Harry Potter and Lucy Daniels,
I like the pictures of the cute animals.

I love playing and watching football,
I find it amazingly cool!
Playing netball is really fun,
it gets even better when played in the sun!

Pick your favourite things carefully,
they'll be of use to you eventually.

Rachael Palmer (11)

My Favourite Things

Watching the warm fire turn into ashes,
When snowflakes fall on my eyelashes.
These are a few of my favourite things.

Oh! and reading a good book,
Going to the shops just for a little look.
These are a few of my favourite things.

Also playing outside with you and you,
Doing crafts, oh and art too!
Jumping in the pool,
Oh it's so cool.
Playing on your holidays every day in the sun,
Isn't going on your holidays such good fun?
Yes of course these are a few of my favourite things.

Going to school and learning about old kings.
I'm afraid that is all of my favourite things.

Mary Kinch (7)

My Favourite Things

Beautiful rainbows stretched in the sky,
The stars when they sparkle up so high.

The sheen of dewdrops in the morning sun,
I love the smell of baked cakes and buns.

Dancing up and down to my music,
On the computer with my joystick.

Exotic holidays faraway,
Being with my family on Christmas Day.

Having sleepovers with my best friends,
The make-up and photos never end.

I love going on a shopping spree,
And sitting down with a cup of tea.

When I play netball and my team scores,
Going to a new place to explore.

On the trampoline soaring above,
Hugging my parents which I love.

Doodles and painting in my spare time,
Writing poetry line after line.

Hannah Dawson (14)

Winter

Winter is my favourite thing,
Snow, hail and frost.
Hearing newborn robins sing,
Seeing my dog get lost.

Snowballing and snowmen,
Snow angels and the after-school rush
You miss it when,
The snow turns to slush.

The snow melts away,
Say goodbye to snow and rain
It looks like summer is here to stay
And can't wait until it's winter again.

Alison Richards (12)

Untitled

Trick or treating and Christmas too,
Ghosts and ghouls jump out and scare you.
Shopping, parties and when Hilary sings,
These are a few of my favourite things!

Presents and treats and PlayStation games,
Hallowe'en parties with pumpkin flames.
Playing with my baby dog, going for a lovely jog.
These are a few of my favourite things!

A hug from my mum and a kiss from Dad,
Playing with all my pets,
Scoring goals in the back of the net.
These are a few of my favourite things!

Top of the Pops and reading books,
Looking at boys with charming good looks.
Going to school learning about kings.
These are a few of my favourite things!

Going on holiday with all of my family,
Watching TV and eating sweets.
These are a few of my favourite things!

Camping in the garden and having fun,
Having fun and playing in the sun.
Visiting friends and playing together.
These are a few of my favourite things!

Playing football and other sports too,
Making things out of paper and glue.
Wearing earrings as well as rings.
These are a few of my favourite things!

Kayleigh Warburton (12)

My Life

I enjoy riding my bike,
That's the thing I really like.
I like going to parties
And eating lots of Smarties.
I love reading spooky books,
And meeting special famous cooks.
I like to dance and sing,
Trying to be a pop star, wearing gold shiny rings.
I like my teacher at my favourite school,
She's really nice, gentle and cool.
I'm always happy when I win,
I keep my secrets in my tin.
Sometimes my dad takes me to the park,
At home I'm not afraid of the dark.
I really enjoy flying a kite,
And my favourite colour is glowing white.
On the sofa I like to relax and sit,
Doing exercise too, getting active and fit.
I enjoy going to school,
And also swimming in the pool.
I like to have a really good dream,
And every day I like to eat ice cream.
I love to wear my best coat
And to float in a little boat.
I like to see the London tower,
And smelling a good flower.
My favourite thing is to have fun,
In the garden, in the sun.
In planes I like to fly,
But sorry now, goodbye.

Jashanpreet Khatkar (10)

A Few Of My Favourite Things

Reading a thick book with hundreds of pages,
Picking up conkers for ages and ages,
Rainbow colours, birds that sing,
These are a few of my favourite things.

Flowers in colourful, delicate shapes,
Freshly made bread that the baker makes,
Precious, beautiful, sparkling rings,
These are a few of my favourite things.

Dew on the spiderwebs, warm shining sun,
Amber sunset when the day is done,
Contented house pets, treated like kings,
These are a few of my favourite things.

Steaming hot puddings with chocolate or custard,
Sizzling sausages (without the mustard!)
Letter for me that the postman brings.
These are a few of my favourite things!

Emma Farrant (10)

I Like, Do You Like?

Visiting friends, camping in the garden,
Dressing as a pirate and playing in the sun,
Parties and holidays are really fun.

I get a kiss from my mum and a hug from my dad,
I catch things with wings while having ice cream.
Don't you like this?
'Cause I like this.

Naim Miah (9)

A Place In The Sun?

I love to travel round the world
To see so many sights.
I love the sun, the sea, hotels,
The excitement of the flight.

Last year we went to Florida,
Five Star all the way.
It made me feel so special,
I loved that holiday.

The year before we went to France,
The food was really ace,
Pastries, frites, moules marinier,
I really loved that place.

Next year Barbados has been booked,
Crystal-clear sea and sun.
I love that reggae music,
Two weeks of total fun.

I really love my holidays,
To London, Paris, Rome,
But the thing that I love most of all
Is always coming home.

Robert Jervis (10)

My Ice Skating

I go ice skating every Sunday and I have lots of fun,
It is always chilly and I don't see the sun.
I put on my ice skates, I put them on tight,
When I first went on the ice, I got a big fright.
I am now on level 5,
Ice skating makes me feel alive.
I've practised and practised and practised some more,
When you look at the ice, it's just a slippery floor.
I can do spins and skate backwards and jump in the air,
I ice skate like I just don't care.
That's my favourite thing and I'll ice skate forever,
And if you go ice skating don't complain about the weather.

Poppy Stone (9)

My Favourite Things

Playing in the garden, having fun,
Running around enjoying the sun.
Carelessly daydreaming about having wings.
These are just a few of my favourite things!

Badminton, swimming and basketball,
Going shopping at the local mall.
Going to school doing lots of things
Like learning about the affects of bee stings.
These are just a few of my favourite things!

Snowball fights in the winter,
Playing my made-up card game called 'Hinter'
Making a variety of things with string.
These are just a few of my favourite things!

Computer games and reading books,
Attempting dishes produced by famous cooks,
Watching films like 'Lord of the Rings'
These are just a few of my favourite things!

Daniel Johnston (10)

My Favourite Things

M y family, full of love and kindness
Y achts on a calm lake with gulls screeching in the air

F riends who are always there for me and are good fun
A utumn when the leaves fall making a golden carpet
V alleys, forests, beaches and mountains,
  nature's amazing creations
O utings, sitting on a bank feeding ducks and having a picnic
U p a large hill or building, looking out over the landscape
R aindrops strewn on plants, like glass beads, after a heavy shower
I cicles hanging from roofs and fir trees covered in a coat of snow
T he sun rising, while the first shafts start the dawn's chorus
E vening, when the sun goes down leaving purple streaks
  like paint strokes.

T hinking, being in an entire world of your own,
  dreaming of anything
H elping people, having that feeling of generosity and pleasure
I n a new place, exploring everywhere and discovering
  unknown things
N ext to a crackling fire, roasting chestnuts and just talking
G eese, watching them fly in a 'v' across the sky on their long trips
S ensing that pleasure of finishing a poem.

Ellen Berry (10)

My Favourite Things

Flopping around all over the house,
After riding my favourite horse.
Vanishing acts I like to see,
Over at my favourite friend's party.
Under the duvet I love to cuddle,
Ribbet the frog my favourite toy.
I like to wear my dancing shoes,
Tapping along to my favourite tunes.
Everywhere I look,
My favourite things.

Emma Rattray (7)

My Rabbit

Where should I start?
She has no limit to her pace,
She absolutely loves having a race.
Her ears are floppy 'n' long,
She also has a cute little tongue.
She mostly eats bright juicy carrots and green
tender lettuce.
You can't forget her furry fluffy bun tail!
She listens to me when I say, 'Go, fetch the mail!'
She is calm and wise,
She has beautiful, beady, brown eyes.
She mostly plays with her small squeaky ball,
It's her best toy of all.
She has gorgeous, golden, black fur.
I love stroking her.
She's got tiny white patches,
And she never scratches.
She listens to me, and understands what I am saying!
She is lovely.
She is my cute, adorable mate.
She hops and sniffs around.
When we play hide-and-seek, I'm always found.
She isn't vicious in the slightest bit.
She's also very fit!
Her name is Anisa.
My gleaming pet rabbit.

Sanaa Rashid (10)

My Favourite Things

Basketball, football, here we go!
Birthdays, Easter, Christmas snow.
Watching fun, emotional DVDs,
Writing poems and cool stories.

Playing on my bike, going to the park,
Watching fireworks give a frightening spark.
Downloading music, playing games,
Going on holiday in big jet planes.

Making my friends laugh, having fun,
Inventing fun games for everyone.
Chilling out is what I do,
Singing along, how about you?

Lauren Greer (10)

Untitled

Where can I start with my favourite things,
I have lots of toys that great pleasure bring.
First is my bike with its speed and its gears,
My bike has got bigger over the years.
PlayStation next with its remote control pad,
Completing levels makes me real glad.
Bike and car games are good fun,
Most of my games are already done!
Out of the house and into the park,
My remote control car is great in the dark.
With lights flashing brightly it travels so far,
That's why I like my remote control car.
My mum, my brother and my best pal Wayne
Went to a country called Spain.
Sun, sea and happy days,
These are my favourites put on one page!

Kane Higham (10)

Tae Kwon Do

My favourite thing is tae kwon do,
I can kick high, I can kick low.
My mum and brother go too,
We are always black and blue,
But it keeps us all fit
And teaches us how to hit.
In the Scottish Nationals I won gold,
'Not bad Joe,' I was told.
I train three times a week
Grandad says that's why I'm so sleek.
He calls me 'stringy legs',
He says they look like clothes pegs.
But when I win he's really proud,
With his little white hair, sat in the crowd.
I practise at home with my mum,
Sometimes she kicks my bum.
Then we laugh so much,
My sides ache to touch.
Tae kwon do is the bestest thing to do,
Why don't you try it too?

Joe Bennison (10)

Dreamer

Eating, sleeping, shopping,
The three best things I do.
I dream about them all the time,
Cinema, TV too.

Animals, parties, discos,
Hanging out with friends.
We share a joke and laughter,
The boys we cannot stand.

My dreams, my thoughts,
That's all I ever do,
As well as keeping secrets,
That's what good kids do.

Hannah Weatherill (12)

My Favourite Things

Winter comes, snow crisp and white,
With woolly jumpers, gloves and boots,
Snowballs, building snowmen big and huge.
Until spring with snowdrops, bluebells, chaffinches,
Long and tall, fresh green meadows
With lambs skipping around.
Red-hot summers, buckets and spades,
Swimming, sunbathing, holidays galore.
Then autumn coloured, gold, red brown,
Leaves tumbling to the ground.
Squirrels collecting acorns for when winter comes.
Conkers, Hallowe'en, fireworks light up the skies.
Then the winter is back again,
My favourite things start all over again.

Corey Joanne Slater (8)

My Favourite Things

My birthday's in May with presents all around,
Games and toys with birthday paper on the ground.
I love my party, sandwiches, cakes and sweets to eat,
My mum's set the table all beautiful and neat.
Party games, we are all jumping around,
When the music stops we fall to the ground.
When the last person's left, they've won a prize,
My mum puts the toy in a box to hide the size.
When the winner opens it, what a surprise!
The doorbell rings, mums and dads are here
To pick up their children who won't appear.
No one wants to go home and leave the fun
All my friends see their mums and dads and run.
Goodie bags given out to everyone!

Ryan Carr (8)

My Favourite Things

Ice cream, sunshine, holidays,
Football, tennis and summer days.
Chocolate, TV, reading and flowers,
Skiing, animals as well as Alton Towers.
Golden jewellery, beaches and art,
Running, rounders, taking part.
I love to go cycling, swimming too,
Not to mention playing something new.
My mom's cooking is always a treat,
And I like my room to be tidy and neat.
Poems, science, the start of spring,
Presents, Christmas and being able to sing.
These are some of my favourite things,
But life itself is more precious than anything.

Keeley Smith (11)

My Family

I really like my mummy,
Her dancing is so funny.

When she tries to bop,
She skips and jumps and hops.

Of my brother I'm quite proud,
He could be in Girls Aloud!

I am a musician,
And I have private tuition.

I really love to sing,
It is my most favourite thing.

My favourite band is The Zutons,
To see them I'd put my dad's boots on!

My favourite sport is netball,
I also like watching football.

These are the things I find quite fun,
So I hope you enjoy my little poyum.

Louise Barclay (11)

My Favourite Things

Diamonds and rubies and lots of warm kisses,
Coats and shoes and most of all wishes,
Winter and summer in a whole lot of love.
These are a few of my favourite things.

Football and tennis and Toys 'R' Us gifts.
Dancing and singing and going on lifts,
Jumping around in a whole lot of fun.
These are a few of my favourite things.

Glitter and fairies and scent up my nose,
Easter and springtime and a beautiful rose,
Babies and children in a whole lot of fun.
These are a few of my favourite things.

Christmas and birthdays and fizzy drinks too,
Getting an ear pierced with a sign of pain too,
Karate and shopping in a whole lot of love.
These are a few of my favourite things.

Jamaica, Hawaii and most of all Spain,
Dancing and swimming it has no pain,
Screaming and shouting in a whole lot of fun.
These are a few of my favourite things.

Weddings and movies and sleepovers, fun,
Mondays and Tuesdays with a water gun,
Flowers and butterflies in a whole lot of love.
These are a few of my favourite things.

Make-up and hair days and sleepovers, cool,
Hanging out with my friends and going to school
Dancing and prancing in a whole lot of fun.
These are a few of my favourite things.

Princesses and princes in a whole lot of love,
Now these are a few of my favourite things!

God's Joy Monene (10)

My Top Four Faves!

Presents, presents I love presents
Wrapped in silver and gold.
It's fun when you open them
Because you haven't been told.

Bacon, bacon, I love bacon,
With extra parts of fat.
What a marvellous treat,
No way am I sharing it with my cat.

Flumes, flumes, I love flumes,
You go whooshing down.
Swirling, twirling, whirling
And no one in the world would frown.

Smudgey-Wudgey, that's my cat,
He sometimes purrs and he loves a pat.
Prancing, dancing, trancing around,
He's the most favourite thing I've found.

Ella Milan (7)

Those Are Some Of My Favourite Things

Tamagotchis are so great,
For me they do fascinate.
Bratz are just the best,
They give me lots of interest.
Chocolate is so sweet,
It's so yummy to eat.
Those are some of my favourite things.

Books are my joy,
I'd rather do that than play with a boy.
Sometimes I like to watch TV,
But if I watch too much people bug me.
I do like to curl my hair,
But only when there's time to spare.
Those are some of my favourite things.

I like to cuddle my pets
And also go on the Internet.
I love to do knitting
And also cross-stitching.
I like to ice skate
And have a laugh with my mates.
Those are some of my favourite things.

Sophie Parkin (10)

Me, Myself And I

Playing in the sun,
Having lots of fun,
Dogs and cats,
Bunny-printed mats,
McFly and Pussycat Dolls,
Crisps and chocolate balls,
My Nintendo DS,
A long satin dress,
Reading my favourite book,
Being cheeky, then let off the hook!
Parties, holidays, discos and birthdays.
These are my favourite things.

Dana Rahimi (9)

My Favourite Things

My favourite things are . . .
Stickers and golden rings!
Teddy bears and all chocolate things!
My scene dolls and racing cars!
Especially those special twinkling stars!
Most of all I really like,
Birds that sing and mountain bikes,
Sparkly crowns and scary wolf hounds.
Here you can guarantee your best toy is found.
In this very special place all your dreams come alive.
You feel like you've dived in a world full of toys,
Where there is something for both girls and boys.
So come with me, and you will see,
I'll show you a place which is full of our dreams!
So catch a train, taxi or bus,
To come and join us in Toys 'R' Us!

Tahmina Alam Shamim (12)

Favourite Things In Life

My dog and my rabbit are my favourite pets,
Once we had to take the dog to the vets.
He had a bad leg and a bad head,
But he was still able to get into his bed.

Swimming is my favourite hobby,
I have a favourite teddy called Dobbie.
I had a fish called Eric,
But my favourite was called Derek.

My favourite colour has to be red,
I especially like it when it's on my bed.
My favourite shape is a star,
Because it follows you wherever you are.

Darcie Lingard (11)

My Favourite Things

What are my favourite things?
Where do I even begin?
My love for anything sweet,
Makes my heart beat.
Dressing up as a ghost or a king,
Wearing a magical ring.
These are some of my favourite things.

What are my favourite things?
Playing hide-and-seek with the twins.
PlayStation games, television and candy between meals.
Dancing like Usher while R Kelly sings,
These are some of my favourite things.

What are my favourite things?
Going to the park,
Leaning against the bark.
Carefully watching the frogs hopping around
Trying to catch their prey.
Oh how I pray that childhood will never end.
These are my favourite things.

Kudakwashe Nyakanyanga (9)

Sing A Rainbow

Sing a rainbow favourite things
Roses smell so sweet
Juice that water can't beat,
The sun shining down from the clouds,
Crystal-clear water from the lake,
Blueberry pies that you bake.

Claire Mackie (7)

My Favourite Things

Adventure stories are my favourite reads,
I also like to do Hama beads.
I like to go to the park and play on the swings,
Reading, Hama beads and going on the swings
Are some of my favourite things.

Chelsea FC is my favourite team,
To play for them is my dream.
McFly is the coolest group that sings,
Chelsea and McFly are some of my favourite things.

I play for Intersport girls,
My favourite chocolates are Twirls.
I really like the 'unknown' the doorbell brings.
Football, chocolate and surprises are some of my favourite things.

Chloe Sainsbury (10)

My Favourite Things

I love to do creative things,
In art we use a lot of string.
I love to ride my nice bike,
There are a lot of things I like.
I love to play computer games,
Maybe one day I'll be full of fame.
I really love my mum and dad
But sometimes they really drive me mad.
I know I know, I know I should,
Be really, really, really good.
Camogie is my favourite sport,
I love to go and visit the port.
I really like the colour blue,
I love the sweets that you can chew.

Aislinn Bryson (10)

Untitled

My favourite things are art,
And imagining throwing a dart.
Cruising with Ciara and her rings,
These must be my favourite things.

I love shouting and singing,
But most people think it minging.
Playing maid servants and kings,
These must be your favourite things.

My favourite thing is skating,
But when I'm not doing that I'm painting.
Wearing Bratz items and their blings,
These must be my favourite things.

Playing baseball
And my favourite sport football.
Seeing who can do the most blinks,
These must be my favourite things.

My favourite things are bowling
I also love rolling.
Designing and making key rings
These must be my favourite things.

Anthea Catherine Kodua (10)

The Best Thing Of All

PS2 and playing on the flumes,
Football in the garden,
Swimming in the pool
And playing at school.

Maths, science and PE,
Do you like those three?
Playing cricket for my team,
Building Lego and watching TV.

Reading a magazine and a book,
Doesn't matter which one
As long as it's good.

Doctor Who in the back garden
Star Wars at the front
But the best things of all
Are my friends.

Jack Gilbert (10

Untitled

Since I was little, I've played computer games,
Mostly with a friend whose name is James.
We also like to swim in the sea,
Eating popcorn and watching TV.
Billiards and snooker create lots of fun,
Especially when you mis-cue, like I've just done.
The conker season soon rolls round,
And the air is filled with conker-splitting sounds.
I like to play for hours on mobile phones,
Never realising it will cause another one of my mother's moans.
Roller skates and skateboards also keep me amused,
Though it's not very funny when you get home cut and bruised.
My friends and I like to cycle in the park,
But with strict instructions to be home before dark.
I like to spend a day at the zoo,
Riding the elephant and picnicking too.
Going around the houses at Hallowe'en,
Dressed in gruesome costumes, creating a frightening scene.
Christmas soon comes, bringing pleasure and joy,
It's a great time for a girl, but I think it's better being a boy!

Tony Hartill (11)

My Favourite Things

I love to play football,
Having a tackle and a fall.
A win for my home team,
Then have a paddle in a stream.
Scoring a goal in the back of the net,
Having great fun and stroking my pet.
I like to race on my bike,
Then have a go on a trike.
My favourite programme is Green, Green Grass.
I like Listening to Kaiser Chiefs,
Lastly, sneakily getting into mischief.

Owen Ricketts (9)

My Favourite Things

I like sherbet lemons with the sherbet coming out, like a bomb,
I like liquorish straws and twizzle them round my tongue.
I like Maltesers they crunch and crackle like a fire,
I like fruity chews because they stick to your teeth.
I like marshmallows because they make your cheeks puff out,
I like candyfloss because it melts in your mouth.
I like bubblegum because you can blow up big balloons,
And pop them and they stick to your face.
These are my favourite sweets.

Hannah Berry (7)

All My Favourites

My favourite things are these indeed,
I've made a list for you to read.
My favourite food is Chinese chicken,
When added to rice it's very nice.
I love to bake a chocolate cake,
Macaroni cheese is my favourite to make.
Melted chocolate licked from the dish,
Salmon is my favourite fish.
Apples and melon are my favourite too,
They're crunchy and juicy and good for you.

A kitten is my favourite pet,
Tara is the cutest I have met.
She's soft and fluffy with a cute little nose,
And sharp little claws at the end of her toes.
When I play with her she lets out a squeak,
Jumping on me with her padded feet.
With a twitch of her ears and a flick of her tail,
She jumps out at the postman delivering the mail.

Hugs with my mum and sharing a seat,
Cooking for Gran and massaging her feet.
Swimming with my brother and having a play,
Spending time with my dad at the end of the day.
Helping Grandma make her garden look nice,
Riding with Ciara on my horse Spice.
Alissa and I like to shop till we drop,
Only when we run out of money we stop.
I hope you've enjoyed reading my list,
I don't think there is anything I have missed.

Heather Hamilton (11)

My Favourite Things

Arts and crafts and everything daft,
Playing with my friends and having a laugh.
Jewellery, bling and rings
Are some of my favourite things.

Roller skating and cycling too,
Acting and doing impressions of you.
Pretending to be loads of people like kings,
Are just some of my favourite things.

Running as fast as I can and playing in the park,
Dancing around and looking at the stars in the dark.
When my favourite band come on I sing,
These are a few of my favourite things.

Presents, treats and pets,
On the laptop surfing the net.
Christmas bells that make a loud ting.
These are just some of my favourite things.

A kiss on the forehead from my mum and dad,
A lick on the cheek from my dog when I am sad.
Playing instruments like the guitar with strings.
Are some of my favourite things.

Becky Preston (10)

These Are A Few Of My Favourite Things

Christmas and birthdays are lots of fun,
Oh I wish my birthday was in the sun
So all my family could come.

I like to read, I like to write,
I like my friends to come and see my art.
I like to dress and act my favourite part
But most of all Easter because of the creamy lovely chocolate.
I like to watch TV in bed.

But now it's time to say goodnight,
So I better switch off the light,
Ready to fall asleep and dream,
Of my favourite chocolate cream.

Demi-Laraine Viccary (9)

My Favourite Things

Books, books are my favourite things,
I read about horses with feathery wings.
About princesses locked up in high towers,
About witches and wizards with magical powers.

Animals, animals are my favourite things,
The powerful lion is supposed to be king.
Zebras and their glorious stripes,
Dogs, there are millions of types.

Food, food is my favourite thing,
From chicken to chocolate to onion rings.
I love ice cream and cake and strawberry meringues,
Fairy cakes, tarts and lemon tang.

Gardening is one of my favourite things,
I like to plant flowers, like bluebells that won't ring.
I like to plant trees and all sorts of bushes,
Some people plant herbs to make herbal juices.

Callum Forrester (10)

My Nan's Birthday

I see you in the darkness,
I see you in the light,
I'm going to see you everywhere tonight.
I see you in the clouds,
I see you in every breath I take,
I see you everywhere.

We're gathered today
On this happy occasion.
This is a moment I will cherish all my life.
Now I'll cut this cake
With a special knife
And now I'll go to the special lake
Where I can remember all the memories of your life.

Today is a special day
Because it's your birthday.
This day means so much to me
Since you have passed away
And I'm wishing you a happy birthday
And all of this is dedicated to you
I love you.

Lots can be said
But I have two words to say to you -
Happy Birthday.

Nazmin Miah (9)

The Best Things I Like To Do

On Hallowe'en I like to go trick or treating at night,
I knock on the door and people scream with fright.
I get loads of sweeties, a whole truck full
I get so many that the truck can't pull.
I like to go to a feast,
There are always nice things to eat.
I love it when chocolate and pizzas are set on a table,
I then eat it up and have a nap in a baby's cradle.
I love to go to the chocolate spa,
I get my friends to go but don't get very far.
I try to push them in
But they just run and hide in a bin.
I like to wake my sister up in the middle of the night,
Where I hide out of sight.
My constant sleep talk wakes her up all sorts of times,
She is so tired that she almost goes blind.
I also like to make poems up,
It's a hobby that I love so much.
Just like this poem, I do my best
I try to make it just as good as the rest.

Jemma Fear (13)

What I Like

I love getting on stage
And performing my things.
Everybody staring because,
It's my time to sing.

I love swimming in the sea,
For me to swim there too.
It's like it's open and wide
For me to go through.

I love so many things,
I can't remember all.
I love my long hair
And being so tall.

These are the things I love and adore
I want you to know I love a lot more.

Chloe Louise Letts (11)

I Like . . .

I like chocolate,
I like sweets,
I like the feathers that tickle my feet.

I like football,
I like me and also
I like my happy family.

I like you,
I like me, myself and I.

Lucy Kailondo (10)

Untitled

Playing football and drawing in art,
Give me joy in my heart.
Singing songs and dancing about,
These are a few of my favourite things.

Playing tennis and winning at chess,
Gives me joy to impress.
Rock climbing and glamorous posters.
These are a few of my favourite things.

Fun sleepovers and wearing make-up,
This gives me time to wake up.
Simpsons on TV, fun to watch.
These are a few of my favourite things.

Bratz dollies and riding my bike,
Make me scared of heights.
Eating at Burger King and burping McDonald's.
These are a few of my favourite things.

Chantell Kayizi (8)

Acrostic Poem

F avourite things are just so funny,
A ll my toys and teddy bears and bunnies
V ery little sticky tape to make a hat for all my dollies.
O ther things are like eating spaghetti with Bolognese
U mbrellas are for the rain and twirling in the sun
R abbits leaping across the grass eating all my carrots
I cy ice cream, licking in the hot sun
T hese are a few of my favourite things.
E ggy sandwiches ready to eat.

T eaching little sisters is what I like best
H appy children, playing, skipping
I cky little babies saying, 'Ma, Ma, Ma'
N aughty little hamsters crawling up my leg
G olden time at school! *Hooray!*
S omething I like is better than the best, can you guess?

Gail Bortey (9)

All Of My Favourite Things

Chocolate, sweets so yummy to eat,
Holidays such fun, relaxing in the sun,
Diamonds and rubies shining in the light,
On Hallowe'en night friends give you a fright.
Pets, pets, pets, what can I say?
Maybe I'll be a vet one day.
My favourite day of the week is Friday,
The reason why - I don't know why.
In the night a shooting star shoots by,
Quick make a wish before it rushes by.
Vanilla, chocolate and strawberry runs through my tummy.
Some of my favourite things are almost gone
So let me give you one more thing.
I love to dance and sing.

Sasha Isaac (9)

Rabbits

Rabbits are furry
Comfy and nice
Black or white
Brown or ginger
Crunching carrots
All day long
Babies being born
In spring
Without any fur
Just plain pink
Running in fields
Keep them as pets
Rabbits are my favourite
Rabbits are the best.

Nada Takal (10)

Hamsters And Rodents

H amsters are fun to play with.
A ny colours and sizes.
M aking room for his bed.
S melly droppings they make.
T aking a piece of food every day.
E ating food and drinking water.
R unning on their wheels.
S leeping in their cosy houses.

A ny rodents are cute to me.
N othing is wrong about them.
D anger for them is when there are cats
     and other animals that like eating them.

R odents are very cute and cuddly.
O ranges and other fruit they like.
D rinking water is sometimes good for them.
E xercising on their running wheels and running is fun.
N ever give up if a cat is chasing the hamster or mouse.
T iny hamsters, big chinchillas.
S ilver rodent fur, brown fur and white fur.

Helen Cheung (9)

About Me!

Hi, my name's Rebecca and I am nine,
At school, in lessons I do quite fine.
I love rabbits,
I have lots of habits.
I bite my nails,
I hate slimy snails.

My friends are cool,
I really hate school.
I love my mum and dad,
Sometimes . . . on special occasions I go *mad!*

Pets, pets, what can I say?
Maybe I will be a vet one day.
My favourite colour is blue,
My favourite number is two!

Now or then
It's time to end
My lovely poem
Without you knowing . . .

Rebecca Penfold (9)

My Favourite Things

Cupcakes and chocolate and scoring in football.
Apples and strawberries and flowers and daisies.
Having some sprinkles on my cold ice cream.
These are a few of my favourite things.

When the cat claws,
When my dogs bark,
When my brother fights,
I simply remember my favourite things
And then I don't feel so bad.

Anita Owereh (7)

My Favourite Things

Biscuits and chocolates and saving the football
Playing my Xbox and eating a pizza
Sprinkles on ice cream and chocolates as well.
These are a few of my favourite things

When my nan dies,
When my pet bites,
When my mum shouts, 'Stop it!'
I simply remember my favourite things
And then I don't feel so bad.

Kenan Ilkhan (7)

My Favourite Things

Playing with big trucks, racing my red cars,
Watching the telly and playing some football,
Throwing the ball when I play basketball.
These are a few of my favourite things.

When I'm bullied,
When my dad shouts,
When my mum screams loud.
I simply remember my favourite things
And then I don't feel so bad.

Tariq Taylor (7)

My Favourite Things

Eating my pizza and playing my PS,
Watching the football and fighting my brother,
Licking some ice cream with lots of sprinkles.
These are a few of my favourite things.

When my fish dies,
When my pet bites,
When I lose a match.
I simply remember my favourite things
And I don't feel so low.

Jamie Penfold (8)

Untitled

Dancing and singing and buying some new clothes,
Kicking my new ball and eating some chocolate,
Dancing and singing and making a tune.
These are a few of my favourite things.

When my nan dies,
When I feel scared,
When the big dog barks.
I simply remember my favourite things,
And then I don't feel so bad.

Seyitan Somefun (7)

My Favourite Things

Scoring at hockey and six shots at football,
Eating some chocolate and publishing my book,
Xbox 360 and PlayStation 2.
These are a few of my favourite things.

When I lose games,
When I feel sad,
When my fish all die.
I simply remember my favourite things,
And then I don't feel so bad.

Jake Watson (8)

Untitled

Smelling a flower and making me itchy,
Skipping and jumping, making me happy,
Boys and girls playing, singing in tune.
These are a few of my favourite things.

When my bird pecks,
When my dad shouts,
When I'm feeling sad.
I simply remember my favourite things,
And then I don't feel so bad.

Mary Asamoah (7)

My Favourite Things

Lovely small ponies and sprinkles on ice cream,
Dancing and singing and writing a story,
Going to McDonald's and eating everything.
These are a few of my favourite things.

When I'm bullied,
When my fish dies,
When my grandpa's sick.
I simply remember my favourite things,
And then I don't feel so bad.

Whitney Gitaari (7)

My Favourite Things

Eating bananas and riding my fast bike,
Playing some football and fighting with pillows,
Dinosaurs running and chasing around.
These are a few of my favourite things.

When I'm bullied,
When the cat bites,
When my cousin's mean.
I simply remember my favourite things,
And then I don't feel so bad.

Jake Thom (7)

My Favourite Things

Sprinkles on ice cream and tea with some biscuits,
Swimming is lovely and so is smelling a flower,
Playing in my room and reading some books.
These are a few of my favourite things.

When the cat claws,
When I'm bullied,
When I'm feeling sad.
I simply remember my favourite things,
And then I don't feel so bad.

Tife J-Akinsiku (7)

My Favourite Things

Coffee and chocolate and ice cream and sprinkles,
Smelling some biscuits and eating some strawberries,
Dressing up with my mum, like a princess.
These are a few of my favourite things.

When the cat bites,
When the bee stings,
When I'm feeling shy.
I simply remember my favourite things,
And then I don't feel so bad.

Ife Oluwa Ogundeyi (7)

My Favourite Things

Six runs in cricket and climbing up fruit trees,
Little, sweet, brown dogs and learning about Egypt.
Being Harry Potter and acting it out.
These are a few of my favourite things.

When my dog dies,
When I'm crying,
When it's raining hard.
I simply remember my favourite things,
And then I don't feel so bad.

Liam Browning (7)

My Favourite Things

M aking things out of thick dry clay.
Y ummy chocolate and sweets, wonderful treats.

F unfair rides high-reaching to the sun.
A ctive I like to be, playing football or rugby.
V anilla, strawberry ice cream, I like as a treat.
O n the computer I'll play computer games.
U nder the swimming pool I like to stay.
R eading wonderful books by best-selling authors.
I nternet I like to spend long hours on.
T o make things out of materials.
E ating lovely roast chicken.

T hings I also love to do:
H olidays I love to go on.
I ndependent I love to work.
N othing I love more than sweets.
G oing on trips with my school.
S ometimes I need to just relax in my warm bed.

Joshua Owereh (9)

My Favourite Things Are . . .

M y favourite things are
Y ummy doughnuts with chocolate sprinkles.

F atty lamb chops with cranberry sauce.
A little pet parrot with bright red wings.
V ery big computers that can do everything.
O range pumpkins for Hallowe'en.
U nimportant trips out.
R iding the waves on a surfboard.
I just love all these things.
T all pipes of pizza with pineapple and ham.
E ating pancakes with butter and jam.

T rying to get the best seat in the cinema.
H ot apple snow with home-made ice cream.
I really love all of these things.
N o homework all week.
G oing out to the funfair.
S eeing all of my family.

James Canniffe (8)

My Favourite Things

Ponies are lovely and so are yummy biscuits,
Smelling a flower and eating sweet strawberries.
Treasures and flowers and lots of jewellery.
These are a few of my favourite things.

When my nan dies,
When my cat goes,
When the big dog runs.

I simply remember my favourite things,
And then I don't feel so bad.

Shirley Ly (7)

My Favourite Things

Chocolate and sweets
Are my favourite treats
I love when my granny bakes
Toffee and caramel cakes.

Football and sports
On Wimbledon's courts
I love to play tennis
At it I'm a menace.

Daydreaming about things
Like cocoa beans with wings
And goblins and gnomes
Who come alive in our homes.

I like family and friends
The fun never ends
Playing snooker and chess
To see if I can be the best.

Causeway and landmarks
Fireworks with bright sparks
Munching on lots of Smarties
Going out to great parties.

Rally cars that go really fast
Motorbikes with flames are class
Listening to music CDs
Watching films on DVDs.

Watching programmes like Doctor Who
Basil Brush and Scooby-Doo
Weekends and holidays
Seem to be the best days.

David Kennedy (11)

My Favourite Things

Ice cream with sauces and riding on skateboards,
Watching the Doctor and playing on my PS.
Being Doctor Who in my big Tardis.
These are a few of my favourite things.

When I get kicked,
When my dog barks,
When I'm feeling mad.
I simply remember my favourite things,
And then I don't feel so bad.

Aaron Stephens (7)

My Favourite Things

Sprinkles on ice cream and riding my pony.
Fighting my brother and smelling the flowers.
Flying my red kite in my back garden.
These are a few of my favourite things.

When my cat bites,
When I fall down,
When the big dog bites.
I simply remember my favourite things,
And then I don't feel so bad.

Kelsey Copeland (8)

My Favourite Thin

Cupcakes and strawberr
Roses and daisies and ap
Sketching my friends whilst
These are a few of my favour

When my gran dies,
When I'm shivering,
When tornadoes come.
I simply remember my favourite thing
And then I don't feel so bad.

Shirley Fuakye (7)

My Favourite Things

Chocolate and football, playing with a pet,
Blasting the football in the back of the net.
Having fun and playing with my friends,
Reading stories which have funny ends.
Daydreaming and thinking pigs have wings,
These are a few of my favourite things.

Sitting back and having a laugh,
After football having a warm bath.
When I'm at school, I'll try my best,
I'll try my best in the transfer test.
Watching films like Lord of the Rings.
These are a few of my favourite things.

Toffee, caramel and sugary sweets,
These are a few of my favourite treats.
Getting prepared to go to my next school,
Hopefully when I get there it'll be really cool.
Mum and Dad and all the happiness they bring,
They are my most favourite thing.

Matthew Reid
My Favourite Things

My Favourite Things

My favourite things
Would have to be
My dogs
Or my best friend's hedgehog.

My favourite thing
Would have to be
My four best friends.
Lauren, Leah, Vanessa and Shannon

My favourite thing
Would have to be
My holiday
Or just going away

My favourite thing
Would have to be
The winter
Where the snow is so white

My favourite thing
Would have to be
Fun
In the sun

My favourite thing
Would have to be
Summertime
Drinking lemon and lime

These are my favourite things
What are yours?

Emma Carlisle (10)

Favourite Things

TV and PlayStation, those are the things I like,
And I also enjoy fishing for pike!
On weekends I like to sleep in,
Only if there is not much of a din!

Christmas and Hallowe'en are special times of the year,
Some good Christmas cheer or some spooky Hallowe'en fear!
Or maybe you like playing with your friends,
Running around in the fields chasing hens!

In the summertime you're out in the sun,
With water bombs having good fun!
On holiday away in Japan,
You will certainly need a bit of a fan.

Flying cool model aeroplanes,
Or maybe just at your Aunt Jayne's!
Technology is another thing I like,
And I also enjoy riding my bike!

Catching snowflakes on your nose,
Sitting at a fire warming your toes.
Taking long walks in the park,
Lighting fireworks in the dark!

Peter Moore (10)

My Favourite Things

I love parties
Guzzling on Smarties.
Being with friends,
Waiting on a letter that my pen pal sends.
Birthdays and Christmases are a treat
Hallowe'en and Easter, lot of goodies to eat.

Snowball fights
Are a delight.
Building a snowman
Who's always called Dan,
With twiggy arms and eyes made of coal.
No good for football with no legs to score a goal.

Walking up to the Blue Lake
A picnic we take.
Walks in wet weather,
I always dither.
Getting soaked to the skin,
No good if your clothes are thin.

These are the things I like to do,
How would you like to do them too?

Laura Davison (10)

My Favourite Things

Having fun in the sun
Eating a big chocolate bun.
Saying funny things in a rhyme,
These are a few of my favourite times.

Skateboarding in the park,
Playing shadows in the dark.
I love my dog and my bird
In the morning they're always heard.

I make tea
Just for me
Yippee
Just for me.

I love to jump up and down
And sing carols in the town.
I go to swim in the pool,
Where it's always nice and cool.

Chloe McCullough (11)

My Favourite Things

Billy Connolly makes me laugh,
So I say goodbye to those bar graphs.
Hallelujah on the guitar,
I am still learning to play the first bar!

Reptiles are the coolest of all,
I also love to play football.
Michael Morpurgo, he is the best,
He is a class above the rest.

The crocodile hunter, he was so great,
But he was killed by a stingray, crikey mate!
My favourite band, it is Green Day,
I listen to them on holiday.

Sea World in Orlando is great,
Shamu eats fish by the crate.
Star Wars Risk is my favourite board game,
Conquering planets which have strange names.

Are these a few of your favourite things?

Michael Gillan (10)

My Favourite Things

I really like sleeping in,
Especially if I could hear a pin.
In football I like doing nets,
I also like to play with my pets.

I like eating chocolate,
The sound of money jingling in my pocket,
I do like walking for miles and miles.
I like it when people smile.
Do you?

I really love playing in the summer,
I really liked it when I was in a hummer.
I like it when I have a good dream,
It's nearly as good as eating fresh cream.
Do you?

I like to play football,
Even more when I shoot the ball.
In golf I like to get a par,
I go on about this even in the car.
Do you?

I really like animals,
Especially camels,
Basketball and football,
And I really like to call.
Do you?
I do!

Leon Gregg (10)

My Favourite Things

My favourite food is chips,
I love them to bits.
Ashley Tisdale is so cool,
She makes all the boys drool.

I love staying up late,
With all my mates.
My favourite sport is football,
I'm very bad and very tall.

Zac Efron makes me laugh so
I'll say bye to all that math.
In July it is my birthday,
I might be going away.

My favourite fruit is grapes,
I could eat them by the crate.
I love going to parties,
I also love Smarties.

These are a few of my favourite things.

Leoni Hill (10)

My Favourite Things

Netball, hockey,
I like doggies.
Christmas, birthdays
These might be a few of your favourite things!

Summer holidays,
September birthdays,
Cakes and sweets.
These could be a few of your favourite things!

Lots of food,
Lots of lovely goods,
Learning about queen and kings.
These must be a few of your favourite things!

Ice skating,
Swimming,
Rugby and hockey,
These are probably some of your favourite things!

Cinemas,
Popcorn,
Fizzy juice is fine,
These I know are some of my favourite things!

Writing on the keyboard,
Sometimes using calculators,
Reading lots of great books,
These are some of my favourite things.

Skiing,
Painting,
I like false nails.
Come on, tell me, which of these is your favourite thing?

Ariane Clarke (11)

My Favourite Things!

I love playing games
And making up names
With my brother Bradley James.

I like Hallowe'en,
I dress up like a queen,
The scariest queen I have ever seen.

I love going away on holidays
And sitting in the sun and having fun.

I like going to parties
And eating all the Smarties.
I also like money,
It's a pot of honey.

I love plaiting my hair
While sitting on the chair
And going outside
And playing on the slide.

I like dreams,
They are like a cake full of cream.
And these are a few of my favourite things.

Shannon Fenton (10)

Young Writers Information

We hope you have enjoyed reading this book - and that you will continue to enjoy it in the coming years.

If you like reading and writing poetry drop us a line, or give us a call, and we'll send you a free information pack.

Alternatively if you would like to order further copies of this book or any of our other titles, then please give us a call or log onto our website at www.youngwriters.co.uk

Young Writers Information
Remus House
Coltsfoot Drive
Peterborough
PE2 9JX

(01733) 890066